Georgin

SPELLING RULES!

Makes spelling stick!

Helen Pearson and Janelle Ho

BOOK
E

Name: _____

Class: _____

Gill & Macmillan

CONTENTS

Gill & Macmillan

Hume Avenue

Park West

Dublin 12

with associated companies throughout the world

www.gillmacmillan.ie

© Helen Pearson, Janelle Ho, 2009

978 07171 4583 6

Advisor: Alison MacMahon

Design by Trish Hayes and Stephen Michael King

Illustrations by Stephen Michael King

SCOPE AND SEQUENCE

Unit	Page	Skill focus					
		Vowels	Consonants	Letter patterns	Morphology and etymology	Homophones/ Confusing words	Topic words
1	6	long sounds, silent e					
2	8				-ed, -ing: doubling final consonant		
3	10				-es, -ed, -ing: rules for adding suffixes		
4	12		words ending in f, ff, lf				
5	14		gh, ph				
6	16	REVISION					
7	18	ea					
8	20				-ion, -ness		
9	22			ge			
10	24			dge			
11	26					confusing pairs	
12	28	REVISION					
13	30			ow			
14	32			er, ur, ear, our			
15	34			sh sound: s, sh, ss, si, ci, ch, ti			
16	36			words ending in ure			
17	38						colours
18	40	REVISION					
19	42				-th	fourth/forth	ordinal numbers
20	44			words ending in ic	-ed, -ing: adding k		
21	46			words ending in al	-al, il-, un-		
22	48				-th, hyphenation		numbers
23	50		double consonants			accept/except, affect/effect	
24	52	REVISION					
25	54		soft g		non-English words		
26	56		soft c	sh sound: ci, sci; sci, sce		sent/cent/scent	
27	58				-ous		
28	60	short y			-y: doubling final consonant	dairy/diary	
29	62				compound words, abbreviations		computers
30	64	REVISION					
31	66	ie, ei				rain/rein/reign	
32	68			ex			
33	70				-or, -er, -ant, -ian, -ist, apostrophes, non-English words		occupations
34	72				suffixes		holidays
35	74	REVISION OF UNITS 1–34					

NOTE TO TEACHERS AND PARENTS

Spelling Rules!
A whole-school spelling programme that makes spelling stick!

Some students are natural spellers. They seem to become proficient spellers without any explicit instruction. But the vast majority of students need formal, systematic and sequential instruction about the way spelling works and the strategies they can use to become independent, confident spellers and spelling risk-takers.

The *Spelling Rules!* programme is based on sound linguistic and pedagogical theory. It is informed by recent research into how students of different ages acquire and apply spelling skills, and how those skills move from the working to the long-term memory. The programme consists of five books.

Spelling knowledge

Learning to spell involves developing different kinds of spelling knowledge:

☆ **Kinaesthetic knowledge**—the physical feeling when saying different sounds and words, and when writing the shapes of letters and words.

☆ **Phonological knowledge**—how a word sounds and the patterns of sounds in words.

☆ **Visual knowledge**—how letters and words look and the visual patterns in words.

☆ **Morphemic knowledge**—the meaning or function of words or parts of words.

☆ **Etymological knowledge**—the origins and history of words and the effect this has on spelling patterns.

Icons used in Book E

The following icons identify the main spelling strategy that students will use to complete an activity.

 Say the word. (Kinaesthetic knowledge) These activities ask students to experience how sounds feel in the mouth and jaw. Changing the positions of the jaw, lips, and tongue changes the sounds we make. Encourage students to pronounce the sounds and words accurately. If they mispronounce a sound or word, they may misrepresent it in writing.

 Listen to the word. (Phonological knowledge) These activities focus on discriminating between different sounds and breaking up words into syllables or individual sound segments (phonemes).

 Look at the word. (Visual knowledge) These activities help students to see how the sound is represented using combinations of letters, and to associate this visual pattern with what they are hearing. Students will develop the ability to know when a word does or does not 'look right'.

 Understand the word. (Morphemic and etymological knowledge) These activities focus on word meanings, word families, prefixes and suffixes, spelling rules, word origins and so on—all of which help embed spelling in the long-term memory.

 Practise writing the word. (Kinaesthetic knowledge) These activities develop students' awareness of the physical movement involved in writing the word. By practising writing the word a number of times and in different contexts, the spelling becomes embedded in the long-term memory.

 This icon highlights useful spelling rules. The rule is always introduced the first time students will need it to complete an activity. There is also a handy summary of important rules on page 80.

 This icon tells students that a special clue or hint is provided for an activity. It may be a spelling, grammar or punctuation convention, or a definition of a useful term.

Book E

UNITS OF WORK

Book E contains 35 weekly units of work. See the **Scope and Sequence chart** on page 3 for more information.

WORD LISTS

Spelling lists enable a spelling element to be focused on. And they provide sufficient examples to consolidate the teaching point. In *Book E*, each unit (except Revision) has a list of twelve spelling words. The core words in the lists have been chosen to support the learning focus and strategies being taught in the unit. In addition, some confusing words and topic words are introduced. The words are listed in order from simplest to more challenging.

SLLURP

Each word list begins with a reminder for students to SLLURP. SLLURP summarises the strategies that will help spelling move from students' working memory to their long-term memory.

Say the word carefully and slowly to yourself.
Listen to how each part of the word sounds in sequence.
Look at the patterns of letters in the word and the shape of the word.
Understand rules, word meanings and word origins.
Remember all the similar words you can already spell and relate this knowledge to any new word.
Practise writing the word until it is firmly fixed in your long-term memory.

SLLURP reminds students about strategies they can use to learn the words

Unit banner features the spelling focus in the context of an amazing fact

Spelling focus highlighted in colour

Sequenced activities—each activity focuses on a specific spelling strategy

List words support the learning of the spelling focus for the unit

Space to practise list words; to write theme words, personal words or extension words; or to practise other words with the same spelling focus. Adapt this section to suit the needs of your class

Icons identify the main spelling strategy students will use in an activity

Spelling tips and rules introduced when students need them to complete an activity

Footer shows the spelling focus for the unit

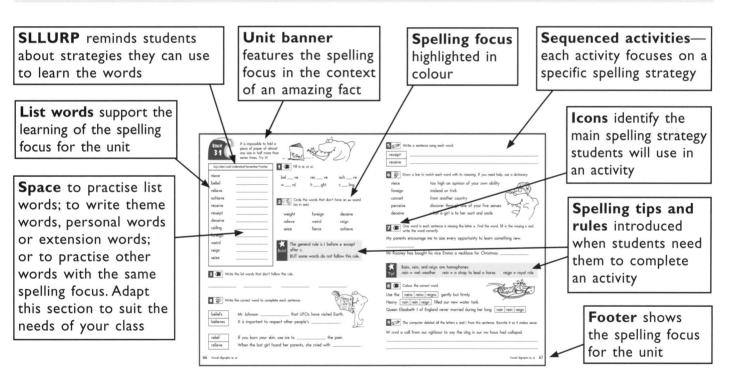

5

In China in 3000 BC, children had powdered smallpox scabs stuck up their noses to make them immune to the horrible disease smallpox. It worked!

Say Listen Look Understand Remember Practise	
realise	_____
suppose	_____
choose	_____
revise	_____
complete	_____
arrange	_____
escape	_____
collide	_____
assume	_____
conclude	_____
declare	_____
disease	_____

1 Group list words using the final vowel sound.

long **a**

_____

_____

long **e**

_____

_____

long **i**

_____

_____

long **o**

_____

long **u**

_____

_____

list words left over

_____

_____

2 Write a list word that rhymes.

cruise   strange   gloom   replied   repair

_____   _____   _____   _____   _____

3 Divide these list words into syllables. Underline the stressed syllable. For double consonants in the middle of a word, the syllable break comes between the double letters. *as/sume*

realise   suppose   declare   revise   arrange

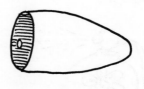
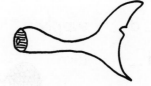

4 ✏ Write a list word for each clue. Then write a sentence using the hidden word.

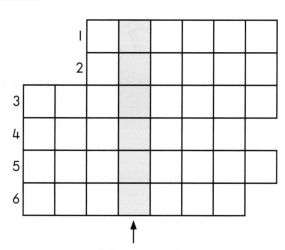

1. do again (to be sure you've learnt it!)
2. make an assumption
3. come to a conclusion
4. put in position
5. finish
6. sickness

Hidden word: _____

Sentence using hidden word: _____

_____

_____

5 👁 Each word is made by rearranging some of the letters in a list word. Write the list word.

clear　　　　　shoe　　　　　peas　　　　　serve　　　　　lice

_____　　_____　　_____　　_____　　_____

6 ✏ Rearrange the words to make sentences.

yourselves can arrange desks choose you how the to

_____

left the people disease to many escape the country

_____

7 👁 Add <u>vowels</u> to make words that match the clues.

r _ sc _ _ 　　save from danger　　　　p _ rf _ m _ 　　pleasant fragrance

pr _ v _ d _ 　　supply　　　　　　　　r _ m _ v _ 　　take away

r _ t _ t _ 　　turn　　　　　　　　　　_ ll _ str _ t _ 　　draw

Unit 2

The left side of your body is controlled by the right side of your brain.

Say Listen Look Understand Remember Practise
begin _____
forget _____
regret _____
occur _____
prefer _____
enter _____
offer _____
answer _____
visit _____
happen _____
target _____
detail _____

1 Each word has two syllables. Draw a line between the syllables. Underline the stressed syllable. *gal/lop*

begin	target	occur
happen	forget	offer

Rule! If the word has the stress on the final syllable, and the final syllable has one vowel, double the last consonant when adding **ed** or **ing**.

occur → occurred   *refer → referring*

2 Complete the table.

add ed	add ing
prefer _____	begin _____
permit _____	regret _____

3 Write three list words that have a short final vowel sound. Write three list words that have a long final vowel sound.

short vowel	long vowel
_____	_____
_____	_____
_____	_____

Rule! If the final syllable has two vowels, just add **ed** or **ing**.

appeal → appealed   *remain → remaining*

4 Complete the table.

add ed	add ing
appear _____	complain _____
detail _____	retain _____

Adding suffixes -ed and -ing to two-syllable words; doubling final consonant

5 Add a suffix to each list word. Use the rules to decide if the final consonant should be doubled.

word	add ed
prefer	_____
happen	_____
enter	_____
regret	_____
visit	_____
target	_____

word	add ing
begin	_____
forget	_____
offer	_____
occur	_____
answer	_____
detail	_____

⭐ **Tip!** A word family consists of words that share the same base word.
act, _act_or, _act_ion, _act_ing, _act_ed, _act_ive, re_act_

6 Complete each sentence using a word from the same word family as the word in brackets.

People sometimes get _____ as they get older. (forget)

Mum is making a special dessert as we are having _____ . (visit)

Rani wanted to learn guitar so she joined a class for _____ . (begin)

Seán said he would meet me at the _____ to the swimming pool. (enter)

7 Use list words to answer the questions.

Which word has a silent letter? _____

Which two words have the same meaning? _____ and _____

Unit 3

The record for piling dominoes is 727 dominoes in one stack.

Say Listen Look Understand Remember Practise
waste _____
blame _____
behave _____
describe _____
recognise _____
remove _____
include _____
hurry _____
deny _____
reply _____
require _____
simplify _____

Rule! If a word ends in silent **e**, drop the **e** before adding the suffixes **ed** or **ing**.

1 Complete the table.

word	add ed	add ing
waste	*wasted*	*wasting*
use		
behave		
describe		
complete		
change		

shark   duck

2 Add **s**, **ed** or **ing** to a list word to complete each sentence.

No one _____ the student dressed as a clown.

"Stop _____ me whenever you lose something!" Vicki yelled.

Each class is _____ to perform an item at assembly.

When a chess piece is captured, it is _____ from the board.

Mr Kennedy always _____ a fun activity in each lesson.

Rule! If a word ends in **y**, change **y** to **i** before adding **es** or **ed**.
Keep the **y** when adding **ing**.

3 Complete the table.

word	add es	add ed	add ing
cry			
hurry			
worry			
deny			
reply			
simplify			

Tip! **Antonyms** are words that are opposite in meaning.

4 Write a list word that is an antonym.

exclude   conserve   complicate   dawdle

_____   _____   _____   _____

5 Proofread this text. There are five mistakes. Circle the misspelt words and write the correct spelling.

Thomas loves writting horror stories. At the begining of   _____

his last story he described a haunted house. Many things   _____

happenned to the hero, including being trapped in the   _____

attic overnight. In the end he escapd and hurryed home   _____

to prove to his worried mother he was not hurt.   _____

Unit 4

A dog has such an amazing sense of smell it can sniff you and tell what mood you're in.

Say Listen Look Understand Remember Practise	
calf	_____
golf	_____
gulf	_____
stiff	_____
sniff	_____
bluff	_____
gruff	_____
proof	_____
wharf	_____
dwarf	_____
engulf	_____
behalf	_____

1 Say each word aloud. Circle the word if you do not say the l.

calf	wolf	self
half	gulf	shelf

2 Say each pair of words aloud. Which pair does not rhyme?

shelf self	half calf	golf wolf	wharf dwarf

3 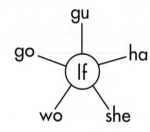 Write the words.

gu
go — lf — ha
wo — she

_____
_____
_____
_____

4 Write f, lf or ff to complete the word.

se _ _   cli _ _   sta _ _   blu _ _   sni _ _

whar _   sti _ _   stu _ _   beha _ _   engu _ _

gru _ _   proo _   flu _ _   dwar _   sheri _ _

5 Make two words beginning with the same letter. Write a sentence using both words.

_____ f   _____ ff

_____

_____

Rule! When a word ends in **f** or **lf**, the **f** usually changes to **v** before **es** is added to make the word plural.

6  Follow the pattern to write the plural.

half → halv + es → halves

calf → calv + _____ → _____

wolf → wol _ + _____ → _____

shelf → _____ + _____ → _____

wharf → _____ + _____ → _____

 Rule! Add **s** to make these word plural.

gulf → gulfs   *proof → proofs*   *chief → chiefs*

reef → reefs   *belief → beliefs*   *roof → roofs*

When a word ends in **ff**, just add **s** to make the word plural.

7 Write these words in the plural.

cliff _____   sniff _____   cuff _____

8 Colour the correct word.

I have so many books I need more | shelfs | shelf's | shelves |.

A | wolfs | wolf's | wolves | eyesight is better than a human's.

Different players scored goals in each of the two | halfs | half's | halves | of the match.

Cliff's | sniffs | sniff's | are loud and annoying.

Can we go to the wharf on Saturday? | Of | Off | course!

9 Write a sentence using each word.

behalf _____

engulf _____

Unit 5

Elephants can talk to other elephants that are kilometres away using sounds that are too low for humans to hear.

Say Listen Look Understand Remember Practise
laugh _____
toughen _____
graph _____
photograph _____
telegraph _____
telephone _____
sphere _____
trophy _____
alphabet _____
phrase _____
phantom _____
physical _____

1 Say each word aloud. Circle the word if gh has an f sound.

cough	ghost	rough
tough	light	laugh
bough	enough	weigh
trough	drought	though

2 In text messages and emails, people sometimes write words as they sound, instead of using the correct spelling.
Write each word correctly.

coff _____ laff _____

enuff _____ fone _____

3 Divide these list words into syllables. Underline the stressed syllable. Write the number of syllables in each word.

graph ◯   enough ◯   telephone ◯   trophy ◯   physical ◯

4 Write the list word that contains each smaller word.

photo _____   ant _____   bet _____

hen _____   leg _____   one _____

5 Some words are easier to understand when they are broken up into parts. Use a dictionary to find the meaning of the parts of these words. What other words do you know that start or end this way?

tele = _____   + phone = _____

The word is _____ .

photo = _____   + graph = _____

The word is _____ .

Other words: _____

6 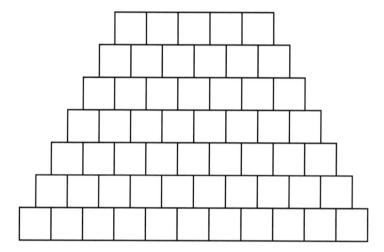 Use the clues to find **ph** words that complete the puzzle. Use a dictionary if you need help.

a stage of development

a group of words

another word for ghost

a wild bird you can eat

a medical doctor

a person who works in a pharmacy

a person who studies philosophy

7 Write list words.

The newspaper article used a _____ to show that crime rates are falling.

Phil's favourite _____ is "rough and ready".

Mia was awarded the _____ for the best and fairest player in the camogie competition.

Unit 6 Revision

Laughter is great exercise. It increases your heart rate, lowers your blood pressure and gives your face and stomach muscles a good work-out!

Ha ha ha

Ha ha

1 An f sound can be written as **f**, **ff**, **gh** or **ph**. Write the correct letter or letters to complete each word.

sni____   whar____   ____rase   rou____   cli____

hal____   lau____   wol____   ____otogra____   dwar____

2 Sort the words into three groups.

answer   complete   excite   trophy   disease   surprise

verb only   verb or noun   noun only

_____   _____   _____

_____   _____   _____

3 Write the plural.

slide _____

graph _____

target _____

trophy _____

shelf _____

belief _____

4 Write each verb so that it agrees with the new subject.

we hurry, she _____

I sniff, it _____

they forget, he _____

you recognise, she _____

I cough, he _____

5 👁 Write a list word you have learnt that contains the smaller word.

refer	here	was	sum	half
_____	_____	_____	_____	_____

have	off	tail	ant	cape
_____	_____	_____	_____	_____

6 Write a list word you have learnt that is an antonym.

exit _____   admit _____   exclude _____

finish _____   giant _____   soften _____

7 ✏ Write the correct form of the word to complete each sentence.

Were you _____ when you won the prize? (surprise)

I had a most _____ holiday last summer. (excite)

We got out of the way when we saw Mr Smith _____ down the corridor.
(hurry)

When our neighbour's cat meows, Rover _____ by barking. (reply)

The football final is _____ right now. I am _____ not bringing a

coat to school as I am not _____ to sit with my class to watch it. (happen,

regret, allow)

8 ✏ Write about the day you had your school photographs taken.

_____

_____

_____

The average person has about 100 000 dreams in their lifetime.

Say Listen Look Understand Remember Practise	
deaf	_____
dead	_____
ahead	_____
heavy	_____
health	_____
meant	_____
instead	_____
least	_____
eager	_____
speak	_____
pleasant	_____
weather	_____

1 Make words using the letters from each box.

r	l	h	thr	spr	tr

_____ead   _____ead   _____ead

_____ead   _____ead   _____ead

l	lt	f	d	th	r

dea_____   dea_____   dea_____

dea_____   dea_____   dea_____

w	sp	st	sn	squ	fr

_____eak   _____eak   _____eak

_____eak   _____eak   _____eak

2 Write the list words under the correct heading.

ea sound as in leaf

_____

_____

_____

ea sound as in head

_____   _____

_____   _____

_____   _____

_____

3 Make a new word. Circle the new word if the vowel sound has not changed.

mean + t   heal + th   read + y   tread + h   seat + w

_____   _____   _____   _____   _____

4 Write a list word with the same meaning.

talk _____

keen _____

unable to hear _____

nice _____

5 Write a list word with the opposite meaning.

alive _____

most _____

light _____

behind _____

6 Write list words.

This New Year's Day we are going to a restaurant _____ of eating at home.

Regular visits to the dentist are important for our dental _____.

7  *Weather* and *whether* are **homophones**. Write the correct word in each sentence.

Dean loves movies, _____ they are dramas or comedies.

I hope the _____ will be fine for our excursion.

⭐ **Tip!**

Lead is a **homograph**. Homographs are words with the same spelling but different meanings.

lead (sounds like bead) = go first, show someone the way

lead (sounds like head) = a heavy metal

8 Write a sentence for each meaning of *lead*.

_____

_____

_____

Unit 8

Before the compass was invented, explorers worked out the directions using the sun during the day and the stars at night.

Say Listen Look Understand Remember Practise	
direction	_____
suggestion	_____
location	_____
separation	_____
confusion	_____
decision	_____
conclusion	_____
greatness	_____
selfishness	_____
stubbornness	_____
cleanliness	_____
forgetfulness	_____

Rule! Some verbs can be changed into nouns by adding **ion**.

act → action

If the verb ends in silent **e**, drop the **e** before adding **ion**.

create → creation

1 Complete the table.

verb	noun
complete	
direct	
	confusion
perfect	
	separation
	prevention
locate	

Rule! If the verb ends in **de**, change **de** to **s** before adding **ion**.

divide → division

2 Write the noun to complete each sentence.

In most sports, the referee's _____ is final. (decide)

Olga wrote an exciting _____ to her story. (conclude)

The _____ of Sammi probably helped us win the competition. (include)

There was a loud _____, but luckily no one was hurt. (explode)

3 Write the number of syllables in each word. Underline the base word.

_care_lessness ③

suggestion ◯   sweetness ◯   adoption ◯   kindness ◯

4 Each word has one or two suffixes. Circle each suffix.

care(less)(ness)

greatness   thoughtlessness   stubbornness   forgetfulness

5 Add either **ion** or **ness** to make a noun. Use a dictionary if you need help.

lazy _____   promote _____   awkward _____

infect _____   careless _____   desperate _____

6 These sentences are too long. Make them as short as possible by using a list word.

Can you tell me in what street or building I would find the cinema?

_____

Writing our project was hard because Tom refused to change his mind about some things.

_____

I often ask my family for their thoughts and ideas for my writing.

_____

Grandad is showing signs of not remembering a lot of things.

_____

All cafés receive a rating based on how clean they are.

_____

The Great Wall of China is so large it can be seen from space!

Say Listen Look Understand Remember Practise
stage _____
bandage _____
large _____
charge _____
sponge _____
bulge _____
fringe _____
merge _____
surge _____
danger _____
stranger _____
siege _____

⭐ **Rule!** When **g** is followed by **e** or **i**, it usually makes a soft g sound.
page   huge   magic   imagine   giant
But sometimes **g** before **e** or **i** makes a hard g sound.
gear   girl

1 Group the words according to the sound g makes.

great	angry	ginger	together
genius	strange	giant	agree

soft g _____   _____

_____   _____

hard g _____   _____

_____   _____

2 Write two words with the same vowel sound. Use a list word and a word of your own.

word	pitch	dirt	shame	wheel
list word				
my word				

Shark
Dark

3 Find three rhyming pairs in the list words.

_____   _____   _____

_____   _____   _____

4 🔦 Write the plural.

word	plural
stage	
bandage	
sponge	
siege	
stranger	

5 🔦 Write the past tense.

word	past tense
charge	
bulge	
stage	
merge	
surge	

6 👁 Make a list word that completes each sentence by rearranging the letters and adding one letter.

There is a _____ sign warning drivers of _____
gear   range

Due to falling numbers, the two teams decided to _____.
germ

7 👁 Rearrange the letters to make list words that complete the sentence.

Angela pushed her _____ off her face so she could see the actors on
finger

the _____ more clearly.
gates

8 👂 Write a list word that has the same vowel sound but a different final sound to complete each sentence.

The blackout was caused by a _____ of electricity.
search

Dad annoys us because he won't _____ his mobile
charm
phone regularly.

The _____ of the castle lasted two years.
seal

Letter pattern ge   **23**

Some strange gadgets have been invented. How about an alarm clock that pours water on you? Or would you rather one that tosses you out of bed?

Say Listen Look Understand Remember Practise	
edge	_____
hedge	_____
badge	_____
ridge	_____
fridge	_____
bridge	_____
judge	_____
trudge	_____
smudge	_____
dodge	_____
fidget	_____
gadget	_____

1 Write the words.

r
br ⟩ idge
fr

_____
_____
_____

f
j
tr ⟩ udge
sm

_____
_____
_____
_____

h
l ⟩ edge
w

_____
_____
_____

a
b ◇ dge
u

_____
_____

Rule! If a syllable has a long vowel sound, it is usually followed by **ge**.
siege   stage

If a syllable has a short vowel sound, it usually has a consonant in front of **ge**.
judge   bridge   edge   cringe   bulge

2 Write **ge** or **dge** to complete each word.

he_____   ba_____   fri_____   smu_____   hin_____

chan_____   mer_____   pa_____   do_____   indul_____

3 ✏️ Use each clue to find a new word.

Rearrange *gifted* if you can't sit still. _____

Rearrange *tagged* to get a useful device. _____

Add g to *bride* to cross the river. _____

Change one letter in *wedge* to make a living fence. _____

Change one letter in *judge* to make it sweeter. _____

Add one letter to *badge* to make an animal. _____

Take a letter out of *fridge* to make a high strip of land. _____

4 👁 Proofread this text. Circle the five mistakes and write the words correctly.

The hamburger took so long to cook that I began _____

to figget. Finally it was ready. Even though I ate _____

carefully around the edge of the lardge burger, _____

the tomato fell out and smujjed my shirt. I _____

quickly got a spunge and cleaned the spot. _____

I couldn't finish the burger so I put the leftovers

in the frige.

5 ✏️ Use the correct form of the verb to complete each sentence.

Uncle Jim is _____ the pet show tomorrow. (judge)

The children are _____ while they wait. (fidget)

We _____ home after a long walk in the rain and discovered Dad had

been making fudge! (trudge)

6 ✏️ Write one sentence using both words.

badge
gadget

_____

_____

Unit 11

Some turtles can **breathe** through their bottoms when underwater.

Say Listen Look Understand Remember Practise	
lose	_____
loose	_____
breath	_____
breathe	_____
desert	_____
dessert	_____
principal	_____
principle	_____
wonder	_____
wander	_____
waist	_____
whether	_____

Tip! Homophones are words that sound the same but are spelt differently.

Some sets of words aren't homophones but do sound alike.
his/he's

Some sets of words aren't homophones but look alike.
lose/loose

1 Circle the pairs that are homophones. Check your dictionary if you are unsure.

his/he's	your/you're
there/their	angel/angle
were/we're	their/they're
lose/loose	whose/who's

Tip! Mnemonics are memory tricks. They help you remember something more easily.

 look, blood

Here are some mnemonics: *Lose an **o** from loose.*
*I'd like a **piece** of **pie**.*
*I'd like a **second** serving of **dessert**.*

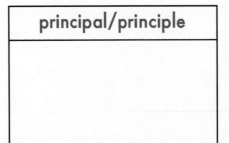

2 Make up your own mnemonics. You can write or draw.

breath/breathe	**principal/principle**	**waist/waste**

3 👁 Write the correct word.

| wonder
wander | Walkers like to _____ in the national park.
I _____ what our new teacher will be like. |

| where
were | This is _____ Abdul hurt himself.
He and his friends _____ skateboarding when he fell. |

| lose
loose | Ellen lets her puppies run _____ in the garden.
She has to be careful not to _____ them. |

| desert
dessert | Grandma makes the best chocolate _____ .
The largest _____ in the world is the Sahara. |

4 ✏ Write a word in each space.

"Y_____ not watching TV till you tidy y_____ room!" Mum told Linda.

Linda had no choice. "W_____ shirt is this?" she asked. "W_____ been

messing up my room?"

"Hurry up, sis!" Brian grumbled. "W_____ going to miss the show. Wonderboy

will meet h_____ enemy and I bet h_____ in real trouble without

Zappa!"

5 ✏ Write a sentence using both words.

| whether
weather | _____
_____ |

| bored
board | _____
_____ |

A cockroach can live up to ten days without a **head**, before dying of starvation.

Hi, Dave.

Tip!

Synonyms are words that have the same meaning.

Tip!

Antonyms are words that are opposite in meaning.

1 Write a synonym.

keen _____

huge _____

nice _____

place _____

completion _____

talk _____

2 Write an antonym.

light _____

behind _____

alive _____

tight _____

friend _____

most _____

3 Write the correct form of the word to complete the sentence.

We liked Casey's _____ that we go ice-skating.
    suggest

The players were so exhausted that they were _____ heavily.
    breathe

The stream _____ with the river and finally flows into the sea.
    merge

"Who will be _____ the contestants?" Trish wondered.
    judge

Dad is always _____ his keys!
    lose

A policeman _____ at our assembly yesterday.
    speak

4 Each clue can be answered using a word you have learnt. Use the clues to find the hidden word and use this word in your own sentence.

1. synonym for talk

2. You walk like this when you're tired.

3. It goes across water.

4. Take care to stay out of _____ !

5. A bull will do this if it is angry.

6. You do this when you can't keep still.

7. It absorbs water.

8. You need it to blow up a balloon.

9. antonym for 'sickness'

Hidden word: _____

Sentence using hidden word: _____

_____

5 👁 Remove a letter from each word to make a new word. Colour the circle if the two words have different vowel sounds.

◯ close _____   ◯ breathe _____

◯ least _____   ◯ dealt _____

◯ meant _____   ◯ whose _____

◯ ridge _____   ◯ brain _____

Unit 13

Cat's eyes glow at night because they reflect light. This makes it easier for them to see in the dark.

Say Listen Look Understand Remember Practise
frown _____
prowl _____
owner _____
towel _____
allow _____
pillow _____
narrow _____
sorrow _____
powder _____
tomorrow _____
coward _____
knowledge _____

1 Sort the list words according to the sound that **ow** makes.

rhymes
with
snow

_____

_____

_____

_____

rhymes
with
towel

_____

_____

_____

_____

_____

2 Change one letter at a time to make the first word into the last word.

moved
_____
_____
towel

prowl
_____
_____
frown

3 Add a suffix to make a new word. Write the meaning of the new word.

own + _____ → _____

Meaning: _____

prowl + _____ → _____

Meaning: _____

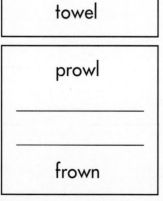

4 Use the clues to complete the puzzle.

1	O	W			
2		O	W		
3			O	W	
4				O	W
5					O	W

1. If a thing belongs to you, you are the _____.
2. Use this to dry yourself.
3. You might do this if you are angry.
4. Give permission or let something happen.
5. Neither broad nor wide.

5 Rearrange the letters to make a word. Write a sentence using the word.

rosrow _____

plowil _____

wormorot _____

dwarco _____

6 There is an error in each sentence. Circle the incorrect word and write it correctly.

We had a pilloe fight. _____

I squeezed into the narro space. _____

7 Add a letter to complete each word.
Colour the ◯ if your word rhymes with sn**ow**. Colour the ▢ if it rhymes with t**ow**el.

grow _ ◯ ▢   scow _ ◯ ▢   throw _ ◯ ▢   fow _ ◯ ▢   show _ ◯ ▢

8  Write a compound word with **ow** for each picture.

_____ + _____   _____ + _____

= _____   = _____

Unit 14

The human intestine can stretch further than six metres!

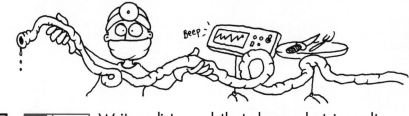

certain _____

permanent _____

turtle _____

return _____

curtain _____

further _____

search _____

research _____

earth _____

early _____

rehearsal _____

courtesy _____

1 Write a list word that rhymes but is spelt differently.

worth   perch   curly

_____   _____   _____

2 Which two list words start with the same letter and rhyme?

_____   _____

3 Write as many words as you can using the letters in the word *permanent*.

4 Use the clues to complete the puzzle.

1. practice for a performance
2. past tense of hear
3. not nearer
4. our planet
5. not late
6. find out about something

5 The two words below have the prefix **re**. Use your dictionary to find the meaning of each verb. What does **re** mean?

return: _____

research: _____

The prefix **re** means

_____

> **Tip!** **Etymology** is the study of the origin of words.
> For example, *cricket* comes from an old French word *criquet*, meaning 'stick'.

6 *Courtesy, courteous* and *courtship* all have the base word *court*. This court is the court of a king. Use your dictionary to find the meaning of each word, then use it in your own sentence.

courtesy _____

courteous _____

courtship _____

7 *Certainly* and *perhaps* express how sure we are about an event happening. Arrange these words in order from most likely to least likely.

definitely not   probably   maybe   certainly   probably not

_____

8 Write list words.

Dad is leaving the office _____ today as he

needs to take me to a _____ for my ballet

performance. It is quite a long journey to the dance

studio and we have to be there by 5 p.m. Mum will

meet us there later as she has _____ to come.

Afterwards we will all _____ home together.

Unit 15

There is so much pressure deep underground that it can turn coal into diamonds!

Say Listen Look Understand Remember Practise
sure _____
assure _____
pressure _____
ashamed _____
cushion _____
fashion _____
passion _____
special _____
ancient _____
machine _____
parachute _____
patient _____

1 Circle the words that have a **sh** sound, as in *sure*. Underline the part of the word that says **sh**.

tension	assume	sugar
suggestion	special	super
blossom	precious	patient

2 Write the words.

```
as
in
en          sure        _____
pres                     _____
                         _____
                         _____
```

★ **Tip!**

A **suffix** is a part of a word that is added to the end of a base word. A suffix can:

- make a noun plural   *pen → pens   ox → oxen*
- change the tense of a verb   *walk → walked*
- make a new part of speech   *fair → fairly, fairness*

3 Add the suffix.

sure + ly → _____   parachute + s → _____

special + ly → _____   machine + s → _____

special + ist → _____   assure + ed → _____

cushion + s → _____   cushion + ed → _____

> **Tip!** A **prefix** is a part of a word that is added in front of a base word.
> The prefix changes the meaning of that word.
>
> **re** = again   *return renew*
> **un** = not   *unhappy unfair*

4 Add the prefix.

re + assure → _____   un + usual   → _____

re + fresh → _____   un + sure   → _____

re + play → _____   un + ashamed → _____

5 Use the letters in each word to write three shorter words. Find one three-letter word, one four-letter word and one five-letter word.

ashamed	pressure	machine	special
_ _ _	_ _ _	_ _ _	_ _ _
_ _ _ _	_ _ _ _	_ _ _ _	_ _ _ _
_ _ _ _ _	_ _ _ _ _	_ _ _ _ _	_ _ _ _ _

6 Proofread this passage. Circle the five mistakes and write the words correctly.

I saw a documentary on televishen last
week. It was about people who had made
jurneys to interesting places. There was a
man whose pashion for insects had taken
him around the world. The next show is on
tomoro and I'm certanly going to watch it.

_____

_____

_____

_____

_____

7 Write one sentence using both words.

ancient
fashion

_____

_____

Even though Mercury is the closest planet to the sun, its temperature can fall to -183 °C — much colder than it ever gets here on Earth!

Say Listen Look Understand Remember Practise	
pure	_____
nature	_____
future	_____
failure	_____
creature	_____
feature	_____
measure	_____
pleasure	_____
leisure	_____
adventure	_____
furniture	_____
temperature	_____

 1 Write the words. Draw a line to link the two words that rhyme.

c
p
l   ure   _____
s   _____
                    _____

2 Write the words. Draw an arrow pointing to the word that has a different middle consonant sound.

mea
lei
plea   sure   _____
trea   _____
pres   _____
                    _____

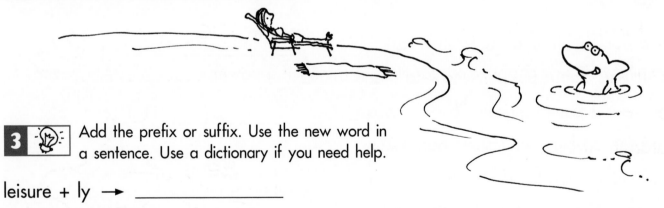

3 Add the prefix or suffix. Use the new word in a sentence. Use a dictionary if you need help.

leisure + ly → _____

_____

dis + pleasure → _____

_____

measure + ing → _____

_____

4 Write the base words.

failure   pleasure   signature

_____   _____   _____

5 Use each clue to write a word ending in **ure**. Only some are list words.

		1	C	U	R	E
	2	A		U	R	E
	3	F			U	R	E
4	L				U	R	E
5	T					U	R	E
6	F					U	R	E

1. to heal, make well
2. sky blue colour
3. It may happen in the _____.
4. time to do what you like
5. precious object
6. tables, chairs, beds

6 Write list words.

Week-long hikes in _____ reserves give my aunt and uncle a great deal

of _____.

The last time I had a fever my _____ rose to 39°C.

My family played Monopoly by candlelight during the power _____.

I wish I could have an _____ holiday
on safari in Africa.

7 Write about an adventure. Use as many list words as you can.

_____

_____

_____

The colours of the rainbow are red, orange, yellow, green, blue, indigo and violet.

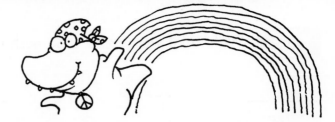

Say Listen Look Understand Remember Practise
ruby _____
scarlet _____
lilac _____
violet _____
emerald _____
indigo _____
crimson _____
azure _____
khaki _____
ochre _____
turquoise _____
sapphire _____

1 The names of colours often come from nature. Group the colour words from the list. Write the common name for each colour in the brackets. Use a dictionary to help you.

From flowers: _____ (_____)

_____ (_____)

From gems: _____ (_____)

_____ (_____)

_____ (_____)

From earth: _____ (_____)

2 Think of other ways to group the colours. Use the space below to arrange your groups. Write a title for each group.

3 ✏️ Write a list word to describe each noun.

_____ sky   _____ lips   _____ sea

_____ land   _____ eyes   _____ blood

4 👁 Use the clues to find a list word.

This colour has all the vowels except **a**. _____

Take one letter from _violent_ to make a list word. _____

Take two letters away from _grubby_ to make a list word. _____

The first syllable of this colour is a mark left after you've hurt yourself. _____

Rearrange the letters in _chore_ to make a list word. _____

Add one letter to _call_ and rearrange the letters to make a list word. _____

⭐ **Tip!** **Similes** compare one thing to another. They say that one thing is _like_ another.
as red as a tomato   _as white as snow_

5 ✏️ Make up your own similes.

as blue as _____   as _____ as _____

as green as _____   as _____ as _____

as yellow as _____   as _____ as _____

as black as _____   as _____ as _____

A tree measured in 1780 had a circumference of 57.9 m. It still holds the world record.

1 Write the plural.

coward _____   cushion _____

journey _____   creature _____

machine _____   curtain _____

ruby _____   patient _____

2 Complete the tables.

verb	add ed	add ing
search		
allow		
frown		

verb	add ed	add ing
return		
own		
assure		

3 Each sentence has one wrong word. Circle the word. Change one or more letters in the word to make a new word that fits the sentence.

I hope that in the feature, greenhouse gases won't be

a problem. _____

"Can you azure me that the leak will be fixed today?"

Dad asked the plumber. _____

"I am curtain of that," the plumber replied. _____

I had to interview my grandparents as part of my

rehearse for a project. _____

The tigers look majestic as they frown in their

enclosure. _____

4 ✏️ Write some unusual colour words for each of the common colours.

blue	green	red	yellow	brown

5 💡 Make antonyms by adding a prefix.

certain _____

usual _____

pure _____

please _____

natural _____

6 💡 Make adverbs by adding the suffix ly.

narrow _____

sure _____

special _____

certain _____

usual _____

7 ✏️ Use the clues to complete the puzzle. Write the hidden word.

1. good manners

2. a soft cloth for drying

3. a precious green stone

4. not ordinary

5. extremely old

6. the day after today

7. let or permit

8. all things not man-made

9. a long trip

10. a worried facial expression

11. maybe

Hidden word: _____ .

Ants have a lot of strength for their size. Some ants can drag objects that are 25 times their own weight.

Say Listen Look Understand Remember Practise	
fourth	_____
fifth	_____
eighth	_____
ninth	_____
twelfth	_____
growth	_____
warmth	_____
length	_____
strength	_____
width	_____
depth	_____
breadth	_____

Rule! Most numbers add **th** to make the adjective form.

1 Write an adjective for each numeral.

1 _____   2 _____
3 _____   4   fourth
5 _____   6 _____
7 _____   8 _____
9 _____   10 _____
11 _____   12 _____

2 Which two number adjectives drop a letter before adding **th**? Write the dropped letter in the box.

_____ ☐   _____ ☐

Rule! Some words add **th** to make the noun form. The vowel or vowels sometimes change too.
deep → depth

3 Use a list word to write the noun form.

warm _____   long _____   wide _____

grow _____   strong _____   broad _____

4  Write list words.

Three words that have a base word + the suffix **th**.

warm   + th →   warmth

_____ + th → _____

_____ + th → _____

Three words that change the vowel or vowels in the base words before adding **th**.

_____   _____   _____

5 Write a sentence about each shape. The first one is done for you.

oval   Half of the oval is shaded.

hexagon _____

pentagon _____

6 Write list words.

Tell me how big the package is. Then I'll know the _____ of wrapping paper I need.

Steel is a strong metal. Its _____ makes it an ideal building material.

7  *Fourth* and *forth* are **homophones**. Colour the correct word.

This is the | fourth | forth | time I've seen this film.

The lion was pacing back and | fourth | forth | in his cage.

8 Write about something with incredible strength. Use as many list words as you can.

_____

_____

Unit 20

Lyrebirds are excellent mimics. They can imitate the sounds of other birds, animals, people and even chainsaws, horns and trains!

Meow

Say Listen Look Understand Remember Practise
basic _____
panic _____
picnic _____
magic _____
mimic _____
logic _____
fantastic _____
terrific _____
gigantic _____
energetic _____
automatic _____
enthusiastic _____

1 Write the list words in the correct group. Some words can be used more than once. Use a dictionary if you need help.

Verbs
_____
_____
_____

Adjectives
_____
_____
_____
_____
_____
_____
_____
_____

Nouns
_____
_____
_____

2 Follow the pattern to add ic.

base + ic → basic

mime + ___ → _____

scene + ___ → _____

automate + ___ → _____

3 Write the list word formed from the base word.

terrify → terrific

energy → _____

giant → _____

fantasy → _____

Rule! s, **ed** and **ing** are verb suffixes. When you add **ed** and **ing** to a verb ending in **ic**, add a **k**. This keeps the hard **c** sound.
picnic → picnicked, picnicking
There is no change when **s** is added.

4 Add the suffix to each verb.

panic + ed → _____   panic + ing → _____

mimic + ed → _____   mimic + ing → _____

5 Colour the right word.

Eric loves | picnics | picnicks | in summer. He usually | picnics | picnicks | with his family in the Botanic Gardens.

When the fire alarm sounded, there was no sign of | panic | panick |. It was only when we saw a rat that we | paniced | panicked |!

Julie is a good | mimic | mimick |. She's always | mimicing | mimicking | her classmates and teachers.

6 Write list words.

Andrea used _____ to solve the puzzle.

The players haven't stopped running yet. They're certainly very _____.

My friends aren't _____ about learning pottery. They'd rather paint.

Mowing the lawn is hard work! Wouldn't it be _____ if someone invented an _____ lawnmower?

7 Write a list word that is a synonym.

enormous _____   imitate _____

Unit 21

In winter, a snowshoe hare's fur changes from brown to white, so that predators have trouble seeing it against the snow. Now, that's a survival trick!

Say Listen Look Understand Remember Practise
final _____
logical _____
magical _____
capital _____
national _____
natural _____
hospital _____
digital _____
criminal _____
critical _____
survival _____
emotional _____

1 Add **al** to the base word to make a list word.

magic → _____

nation → _____

nature → _____

survive → _____

2 Write the base words. Use a dictionary if you need help.

logical _____

emotional _____

criminal _____

Tip! Adding **al** to a word usually changes it to an adjective. Some words ending in **al** are both nouns and adjectives.

3 Write the list words that are nouns. Put an asterisk next to the ones that can also be adjectives.

_____ _____ _____ _____ _____

4 Choose one of the words in question 3 which can be both a noun and an adjective. Write a sentence for each usage.

Noun: _____

_____

Adjective: _____

_____

Words ending in al; suffix -al; prefixes il-, un-

5 🦻 Find a smaller word in each list word.

final   logical   digital   national   emotional

_____   _____   _____   _____   _____

6 👁 Rearrange the letters to make an **al** word that completes each sentence. Only one of the words is a list word!

The Danish _____ family lives in Copenhagen, the _____ city of
              oyral   tapical
Denmark.

The _____ shops hold a street market once a month.
     caoll

Dogs are good pets because they are _____ .
                                     alloy

Mum collects vases in which to display her _____ arrangements.
                                        lofral

Regular _____ exercise is both fun and healthy.
          cailshyp

7 🦻 Add the prefix **il** or **un** to make an antonym.
Use a dictionary if you need help.

_____natural   _____logical   _____emotional

8 👁 Proofread this recount. There are five mistakes. Circle them and write the correct spelling.

Tracey and Adam went to Dublin, our nashional   _____

capital. First they visited St Stephen's Green, which they   _____

thought was a magickal place. Then they went for a   _____

bike ride. Unluckly Tracey fell off and broke her ankle.   _____

She had to go to the hospitle even though her injury   _____

wasn't critickle.

Unit 22

Some experts say that at least one thousand million grams of space dust rain down on Earth every day.

Say Listen Look Understand Remember Practise
eleven _____
twelve _____
thirteen _____
fourteen _____
fifteen _____
twenty _____
thirty _____
forty _____
fifty _____
hundred _____
thousand _____
million _____

1 Write a list word for each numeral.

11 _____   12 _____

13 _____   15 _____

★ Tip! Numbers from 13 to 19 end in **teen**.

2 Add **teen** to these numbers.

14   four + teen ⟶ _____

16   _____ + teen ⟶ _____

17   seven + _____ ⟶ _____

18   eight + _____ ⟶ _____

19   _____ + _____ ⟶ _____

3 Write the word for each number. Circle the part of the word that is the same for each pair.

13 _____	15 _____	16 _____	18 _____
30 _____	50 _____	60 _____	80 _____

4 Write the word for the number.

10   100   1000   1 000 000

_____   _____   _____

★ Tip! Numbers ending in 0 between 20 and 90 end in **ty**.

5 Cross out the letter that is left out when **ty** is added. Write the word and the numeral.

four + ty ⟶ _____ _____

eight + ty ⟶ _____ _____

48   Suffix -th; hyphenation; topic words: numbers

6 ✏️ Write the word for the numeral.

33 _____	44 _____	81 _____
57 _____	28 _____	99 _____
65 _____	72 _____	46 _____

Rule! To make a number into an adjective, **th** is usually added.
Numbers that end in **ty** change **y** to **i** and add **eth**.
twenty → *twentieth*   *sixty* → *sixtieth*

7 Write the adjective for each numeral.

7 _____	10 _____	14 _____
30 _____	40 _____	50 _____
21 _____	82 _____	75 _____

8 ✏️ Write a number or number adjective to complete each sentence.

Some people believe Friday the _____ is an unlucky day.

There are one _____ years in a century.

There are one _____ years in a millenium.

My mum is _____ years old and my dad is _____ years old.

Unit 23

If a cat has hair standing up on its body and tail and its back is arched, watch out — it's aggressive!

Say Listen Look Understand Remember Practise
accept _____
appear _____
effect _____
accuse _____
approach _____
announce _____
possess _____
embarrass _____
necessary _____
recommend _____
occasion _____
aggressive _____

1 👁 Write a list word to match each shape.

Rule! g and c make their soft sound when they are followed by e or i.

2 👂 Circle the word in each pair that includes a soft consonant sound.

suggest	aggressive	accent	recount
accuse	accept	occasion	accident

3 👁 These sentences have too many double letters. Rewrite each sentence correctly.

I've allways bellieved that ice-cream is neccessarry for good health.

_____

There's a speccial occassion this Saturday. It's Grandpa's seventty-fifth birthday!

_____

Double consonants; confusing pairs accept/except, affect/effect

4 ✏️ Add a prefix to make an antonym.

_____ + appear ➔ _____   _____ + necessary ➔ _____

5 ✏️ Add a suffix to make the correct form of the verb.

The lights turned red as I _____.
 approach

I _____ Nina of taking my cap but in fact, I had left it at home.
 accuse

Tomorrow the principal is _____ who the school captain will be. I think
 announce

it will be Cassie because she _____ all the right qualities.
 possess

⭐ **Tip!**

Except and **accept** are often confused.
except = not including   *accept* = take or receive
Affect and **effect** are also often confused.
affect = to cause a change in something   *effect* = a result

---

6 👁️ Write the correct words to complete each sentence.

| accept |
| except |

Everyone in the family _____ her grandmother was in the hall
to see Ellen _____ her award.

| affect |
| effect |

The things we do _____ the environment. Pollution has a
long-lasting _____ .

7 👁️ Use the clues to write a list word.

Which word has a donkey in it? _____

Which word has a fruit in it? _____

In which word is the name for a person, place or thing? _____

Unit 24 Revision

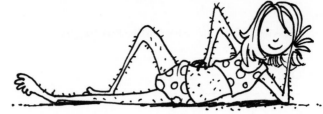

Adults have around five **million** hairs all over their bodies — that's about the same number as a gorilla!

1 👁 Write the missing words.

```
┌──────────────────────────┐  ↑
│                          │  40 m
│                          │  ↓
└──────────────────────────┘
←──────── 120 m ────────→
```

The _____ of the rectangular field is 120 metres.

Its _____ is 40 metres.

The breadth of something is the same as its _____ .

2 ✏ Write a number word or number adjective to complete each sentence.

There are _____ letters in the English alphabet, of which _____ are consonants. The _____ letter is a and the _____ one is e.

There are three _____ and _____ days in a leap year. A year is divided into _____ months. August, the _____ month, has _____ days.

3 Write an adjective by adding **al**.

magic   logic   nation   emotion

_____   _____   _____   _____

4 👁 Write double consonants to complete each word.

a ___ roach   a ___ use   po ___ e ___   su ___ est   emba ___ a ___

5 ✏ Use each word in a sentence.

accept _____

except _____

6 🖊 Use the clues to complete the puzzle.

1. She went to _____ by ambulance.
2. It's great! It's _____!
3. A heater provides _____ when it's cold.
4. You win silver if you come _____.
5. The organiser will _____ the winner last.
6. Something that makes sense is _____.
7. Amhrán na bhFiann is Ireland's _____ anthem.
8. There are _____ days in April.

Ants have great _____ for their size.

7 🖊 Replace the underlined word or words with a more interesting list word you have learnt. Rewrite the sentence using the correct form of the new word.

I <u>think</u> Dad will have packed a boring lunch – again!

_____

Grandpa has a watch that winds <u>without him having to do it</u>.

_____

We love our dog, but he barks whenever a stranger <u>comes near</u> the house.

_____

8 🖊 Write the correct form of the word to complete each sentence.

Mr Chang _____ when he _____ he had lost his keys.
        panic   realise

Grandma always _____ Dad by telling stories of his childhood.
           embarrass

Touch rugby has only a few _____ rules.
        base

The average Irish person eats around 9 kilograms of chocolate each year. That's a lot of Easter eggs!

Say Listen Look Understand Remember Practise
germ _____
ginger _____
gently _____
general _____
average _____
generous _____
religion _____
intelligent _____
generation _____
advantage _____
emergency _____
gymnasium _____

1 Circle the letter g if it has a soft sound.

danger   regret   germ

eager   gigantic   logical

2 Write a list word that contains the smaller word.

rage _____

ration _____

tell _____

merge _____

van _____

era _____

gene _____

3 Group the list words as nouns, adjectives and adverbs. Use a dictionary if you need help. (Three words can be used as both nouns and adjectives.)

noun

_____   _____

_____   _____

_____   _____

_____   _____

_____

adjective

_____   _____

_____

adverb

_____

4 Add **ly** to make adverbs.

generous _____   intelligent _____

general _____   gentle _____

5 Make antonyms by adding **dis** or **un** as a prefix.

intelligent _____   advantage _____

6 Choose the correct word to complete each sentence.

| gymnast   gymnastics   gymnasium |

A _____ is a place where you do various sports and exercises.

_____ is a sport which includes vaulting and tumbling. You need to

be strong to be a _____ .

7 Circle the word or words that do not make sense.
Write a list word that you could use instead.

Gerard is very mean. He always shares things with his friends. _____

I can hear sirens. Get out of the way! There must be an emerald. _____

Angie has an adverb because she's played this game before. She'll probably do very

well. _____

8 Write about one intelligent thing or one generous thing you have done.

_____

_____

_____

Unit 26

Mother seals recognise their babies by their scent.

Say Listen Look Understand Remember Practise

since	_____
circle	_____
centre	_____
cinema	_____
recent	_____
sincere	_____
science	_____
scent	_____
scenery	_____
scissors	_____
delicious	_____
conscious	_____

1 Here are some list words from other units. Sort them into two groups.

excite   physical   recognise

location   emergency   certain

soft c sound	hard c sound

2 Write the list word that contains the smaller word.

scene _____

cent _____

since _____

3 Write the plural.

circle _____   cinema _____   scissors _____

4 Add ly to make the adverb.

recent _____   sincere _____   conscious _____

5 Write a list word that is a synonym.

smell _____   middle _____   yummy _____

6 Use all the list words to complete the puzzle.

7 Make as many words as you can using the letters from the word *delicious*.

____

____

8 *Sent, cent* and *scent* are **homophones**. Write the correct word to complete each sentence.

My uncle ______________ me some Australian five ______________ coins to add to my collection.

Mum put fresh flowers in a vase and there was a strong ______________ in the house.

9 Find three errors in these instructions. Write each word correctly.

To make a cone, you start with a circel. Draw a line from one edge to the sentre. Use sissors to cut along the line. Pull one edge over the other edge and glue them together.

____

____

____

Unit 27

A skunk will spray you with very smelly liquid if you make it nerv**ous**!

Say Listen Look Understand Remember Practise	
fam**ous**	_____
nerv**ous**	_____
danger**ous**	_____
jeal**ous**	_____
courage**ous**	_____
seri**ous**	_____
furi**ous**	_____
cauti**ous**	_____
envi**ous**	_____
preci**ous**	_____
spaci**ous**	_____
vari**ous**	_____

1 Write the list word that comes from the same word family.

vary _____

courage _____

space _____

fame _____

danger _____

envy _____

nerve _____

jealousy _____

fury _____

caution _____

2 Colour the correct word.

Words that end in **ous** are | adjectives | nouns | adverbs |.

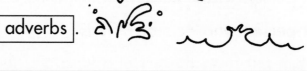

Rule!

When the base word ends in silent **e**, drop the **e** before adding **ous**.
fame → famous

If the base word ends in **ce**, change the **e** to **i** before adding **ous**.
space → spacious

3 Make an adjective by adding the suffix **ous**.

nerve → _____   grace → _____

ridicule → _____   vice → _____

 **Rule!** If the base word ends in **ge**, keep the **e** when adding **ous** to keep the **g** sound soft.
courage → courageous

4 Make an adjective by adding the suffix **ous**.

outrage → _____   advantage → _____

 Rule! If the base word ends in **y**, change **y** to **i** before adding **ous**.
envy → envious   vary → various

5 Make an adjective by adding the suffix **ous**.

fury → _____   mystery → _____

6 Write list words.

A person who is well-known is _____.

A person who is extremely angry is _____.

A person who doesn't take risks is _____.

A person who wants what someone else has is _____.

A person who acts bravely is _____.

7 Write list words.

Recently I watched a programme about a _____ athlete. She had suffered a _____ accident which caused her to lose both legs. However, she was very _____ . She overcame her disability to represent her country in the Paralympic Games. In an interview, she said that she still felt _____ and had butterflies in her stomach before each race. The medals she has won at the Games and in other competitions are among her most _____ possessions.

Unit 28

Nobody knows for certain how the pyramids in Egypt were built. It remains a mystery!

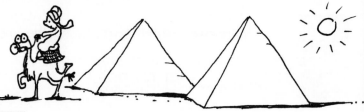

Say Listen Look Understand Remember Practise
furry _____
woolly _____
weary _____
guilty _____
shiny _____
icy _____
sorry _____
fantasy _____
variety _____
mystery _____
system _____
pyramid _____

1 Add **y** to these words to make adjectives.

hair _____   boss _____   dust _____

_____   _____   _____

risk _____   guilt _____   dirt _____

_____   _____   _____

Rule! If the word has a single vowel followed by a single consonant, double the consonant before adding **y**.
mud → muddy

2 Write the correct word.

fur → _____

fog → _____

spot → _____

Rule! If the word ends in silent **e**, drop the **e** before adding **y**.
juice → juicy   *craze → crazy*

3 Add **y** to these words.

noise → _____   scare → _____

ice → _____   shine → _____

4 What is the weather like?

_____   _____   _____   _____   _____

60   Suffix -y; doubling final consonant; short y sound; confusing pair dairy/diary

5 ✏️ Rewrite each sentence, replacing the underlined word with a list word.

Troy was <u>regretful</u> that his ball had broken his neighbour's window.

_____

Grandma's patchwork quilts have a <u>mixture</u> of colours and patterns.

_____

Mrs Doherty feels <u>tired</u> because she has a very young baby.

_____

What happened to Sally's keys is a <u>puzzle</u>.

_____

6 🎧 The vowel sounds in each sentence are missing. Rewrite each sentence, adding the missing letters.

M nt s knttng m sm wlly glvs fr wntr.

_____

M brthr thnks m drm f bcmng fms s fnts.

_____

Th prmds n gpt r thsnds f yrs ld.

_____

r schl prncpl spk t s bt th nw lnch sstm.

_____

7 💭 Dairy and diary are sometimes confused. Write the meaning of each word.

dairy: _____

diary: _____

8 👁️ Colour the correct word.

I'm furious with my sister because she peeked in my | dairy | diary |.

Did you know that | dairy | diary | products are good for your bones?

Unit 29

The first computers weighed thousands of kilograms and were the size of a large room!

Say Listen Look Understand Remember Practise
computer _____
laptop _____
email _____
Internet _____
mobile _____
keyboard _____
programme _____
icon _____
download _____
insert _____
delete _____
barcode _____

1 Write the list word for each picture.

_____   _____   _____

2 Write the correct label for each part of the computer.

| monitor | mouse | keyboard | screen |

_____

_____

_____

_____

★ **Tip!** **Compound words** are two whole words joined together to form a new word.

soft + ware → software

3 Use a dictionary to find the meaning of *ware*.

ware = _____

Write another computer compound word that ends in *ware*. _____

4 Write the list words that are compound words.

_____   _____   _____   _____

5 The same object may have different names in different countries. A mobile phone is also called a handphone or a cellphone. Use the Internet to find out which countries use each word.

cellphone _____   handphone _____

Tip! Many terms or phrases are abbreviated to the first letter of each word.
IT = information technology

6 Unscramble the letters to make the full name for each abbreviation.

PC   aspolner pertumoc _____

WWW   olwrd diew wbe _____

CD   camtpoc cids _____

ROM   eard lony moremy _____

URL   valniseru reecrosu rocatol _____

7 The names of Irish counties are abbreviated on car registration plates.
Write the full county name for each abbreviation.

MH _____   DL _____

C _____   SO _____

G _____   KE _____

8 Abbreviations are sometimes used in email and text messages. Write the full text for each
abbreviation.

LOL _____   ASAP _____

BTW _____   OTOH _____

9 Write the correct form of a list word to complete each sentence.

I spend time every afternoon _____ my cousin overseas.

_____ help managers check the goods in their stores.

Our computer at home is _____ so that Mum and Dad can check what

we're using it for.

_____ big files from the Internet can take a long time.

Oh no! I think I've accidentally _____ the research I'd done on dolphins.

Unit 30 Revision

Murphy the donkey was given the Purple Cross in honour of all the courage**ous** donkeys that carried wounded troops at Gallipoli.

1 Circle the soft c or g sounds. Underline the hard c or g sounds.

ginger   circle   garage   gigantic   success

2 Write the correct homophone to complete each sentence.

[scent   sent   cent]

I _____ Uncle Harry a birthday card last week.

Eucalyptus oil gives off a very strong _____.

In America, a one-_____ coin is called a penny.

[scene   seen]

The _____ at the sale was chaotic. Everyone wanted to be served first.

My neighbour's Old English sheepdog is the largest dog I've ever _____.

3 Write a word ending in **ous** to describe each character.

Pedro always wants to find out more about things. He is _____.

Janet is feeling _____ about having to welcome the visitor.

My dog Max gets very _____ whenever I play with my cat.

When Lara discovered her sister had been secretly reading her emails, she was _____.

4 Make compound words by using one word from each box.

key	lap	down	soft	bar
ware	load	board	code	top

_____   _____   _____

5 Write the adjective form of the word by adding **y** or **ous**.

fur   shine   danger   vary   envy

_____ _____ _____ _____ _____

6 Complete each sentence using a word ending in **y**.

My aunt and uncle are _____ because their sick baby has been keeping them awake at night.

"Have you seen my project, Mum? I can't figure out where it's gone. It's a _____."

I've bought Grandma a soft _____ scarf for her birthday.

7 Circle the word that does not make sense in each sentence. Write the correct word.

Rita is very general. She always shares her things and finds ways to help others.

_____

Ian's been training for the competition sincere the summer. _____

Don't forget to delete the address or the email can't be sent. _____

8 Proofread this text. Circle the five errors and write the correct spelling.

Janice is a computer genious. Resently she took part in a competition to write a proggramme. Although she didn't win she did better than avrage. When she was interviewed for our school newsletter, she said it was important to have a logical sisterm and to be organised.

_____ _____ _____ _____ _____

It is impossible to fold a piece of paper of almost any size in half more than seven times. Try it!

Say Listen Look Understand Remember Practise
niece _____
belief _____
relieve _____
achieve _____
receive _____
receipt _____
deceive _____
ceiling _____
foreign _____
weird _____
reign _____
seize _____

1 Fill in **ie** or **ei**.

bel ___ ve   rec ___ ve   ach ___ ve

w ___ rd   h ___ ght   c ___ ling

2 Circle the words that don't have an **ee** sound (as in *see*).

weight   foreign   deceive

relieve   weird   reign

seize   fierce   achieve

Rule! The general rule is **i** before **e** except after **c**.
BUT some words do not follow this rule.

3 Write the list words that don't follow the rule.

_____   _____   _____   _____

4 Write the correct word to complete each sentence.

beliefs
believes

Mr Johnson _____ that UFOs have visited Earth.

It is important to respect other people's _____.

relief
relieve

If you burn your skin, use ice to _____ the pain.

When the lost girl found her parents, she cried with _____.

5 Write a sentence using each word.

receipt	_____
receive	_____

6 Draw a line to match each word with its meaning. If you need help, use a dictionary.

niece   too high an opinion of your own ability

foreign   mislead or trick

conceit   from another country

perceive   discover through one of your five senses

deceive   what a girl is to her aunt and uncle

7 One word in each sentence is missing the letter **e**. Find the word, fill in the missing **e** and write the word correctly.

My parents encourage me to size every opportunity to learn something new.

_____

Mr Rooney has bought his nice Emma a necklace for Christmas. _____

> ⭐ **Tip!** Rain, rein, and reign are homophones.
> *rain* = wet weather   *rein* = a strap to lead a horse   *reign* = royal rule

8 Colour the correct word.

Use the | rains | reins | reigns | gently but firmly.

Heavy | rain | rein | reign | filled our new water tank.

Queen Elizabeth I of England never married during her long | rain | rein | reign |.

9 The computer deleted all the letters **e** and **i** from this sentence. Rewrite it so it makes sense.

W rcvd a call from our nghbour to say the clng in our nw hous had collapsd.

_____

_____

Unit 32

Cheetahs are **ex**tremely fast over short distances. They can reach 100 km/h when chasing prey.

BOING

Say Listen Look Understand Remember Practise
exact _____
example _____
exaggerate _____
explain _____
expensive _____
exercise _____
excite _____
excellent _____
except _____
exhausted _____
extinction _____
extremely _____

1 Which **c** is the odd one out? Circle it.

excite   excuse   exercise   except

Explain your choice.

_____

Use this word in a sentence.

_____

_____

2 What does the letter **X** stand for in each example?

Xmas _____

on a map _____

at the end of a letter _____

on the face of a clock _____

3 Use one syllable from each column to form list words.

ex	cel	sive
	er	tion
	pen	ly
	treme	lent
	am	cise
	tinc	ple

_____   _____

_____   _____

_____   _____

4 Write the list word that has a stronger meaning than each common word.

very   same   good   tired

_____   _____   _____   _____

5 How many words can you make using the letters from these list words? Look for words that are three, four, or five letters long. Give yourself one point for each word, then a bonus point for each word that includes the letter **x**.

explain	exaggerate	exhausted	expensive

points: _____   points: _____   points: _____   points: _____

6 Add suffixes to these words.

	explain	exaggerate	exercise	examine
add ed				
add ing				

7 Write the correct form of the word **excite** in each space.

Lucas was going to Poland with his family to visit his relatives. I had never seen him

so _____ before. This was his first time on an aeroplane and the first time

he would see his cousins. I guess that is quite _____ !

★ **Tip!** **Anagrams** are words that have the same letters arranged in a different order. For example, *red raw* is an anagram of *drawer*.

8 Write a list word that is an anagram of *expect*.

_____

Write some more words that are anagrams. They don't have to start with **ex**.

Unit 33

Several centuries ago, barbers also did the work of surgeons and dentists.

Say Listen Look Understand Remember Practise
author _____
grocer _____
carpenter _____
lawyer _____
assistant _____
accountant _____
electrician _____
politician _____
journalist _____
pharmacist _____
chef _____
pilot _____

1 ✏ Use the picture as a clue for each occupation.

_____ _____ _____

_____ _____ _____

_____ _____ _____

⭐ Tip!

The names of occupations are often base words with a suffix added.

wait + er → waiter   serve + ant → servant
music + ian → musician   art + ist → artist

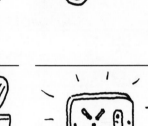

2 👆 Write the base word.

lawyer _____   assistant _____

engineer_____   politician _____

journalist _____   accountant _____

physiotherapist _____ farmer _____

electrician _____   pharmacist _____

builder _____   actor _____

3 Each word has the wrong ending. Write each word correctly.

docter _____   photographist _____

magicist _____   dentant _____

instructant _____   drivor _____

⭐ **Rule!**

Apostrophes can be used to show who something belongs to.
In other words, apostrophes can show **possession**.
the pilot's suitcase (one pilot + one suitcase)
the pilot's duties (one pilot + more than one duty)
When the owner is plural, the apostrophe comes **after** the plural.
When the plural ends in **s**, do not add a second **s** after the apostrophe.
the pilots' uniforms (more than one pilot + more than one uniform)
the children's toys (more than one child + more than one toy)

---

4 Add the missing apostrophes. Circle the words where the apostrophe does not show possession.

I needed a present for my friends birthday, so I thought Id look in Mr and Mrs Jones new bookshop. Its called The Reading Room. It was crowded but I could tell from the customers smiles that they were enjoying themselves. The displays bright colours made the books look exciting. I saw one boys mother buy him four books! Im sure the shop will be a success.

⭐ **Tip!**

Some English words come from other languages.
Chef and *chauffeur* are French words.

---

5 Complete the table. Use a dictionary if you need help.

	meaning	synonym
chef	_____	_____
chauffeur	_____	_____

Unit 34

An American boy once boarded a train alone and travelled 160 km — in his sleep!

Say Listen Look Understand Remember Practise
travel _____
relax _____
journey _____
caravan _____
luggage _____
budget _____
museum _____
attraction _____
entertainment _____
accommodation _____
sightseeing _____
restaurant _____

1 Break each word up into its base word and suffix.

	base word	suffix
attraction		
entertainment		
accommodation		

2 These words can all be used in different ways. Tick two boxes to show which ways they can be used.

	noun	verb	adjective
travel	☐	☐	☐
relaxing	☐	☐	☐
journey	☐	☐	☐
budget	☐	☐	☐
sightseeing	☐	☐	☐

3 Complete the table.

word	add s or es	add ed	add ing
relax	_____	_____	relaxing
journey	journeys	_____	_____
budget	_____	budgeted	_____
travel	travels	_____	_____

Which words are spelt differently in American English?

_____ _____

4 Write a word that matches the definition.

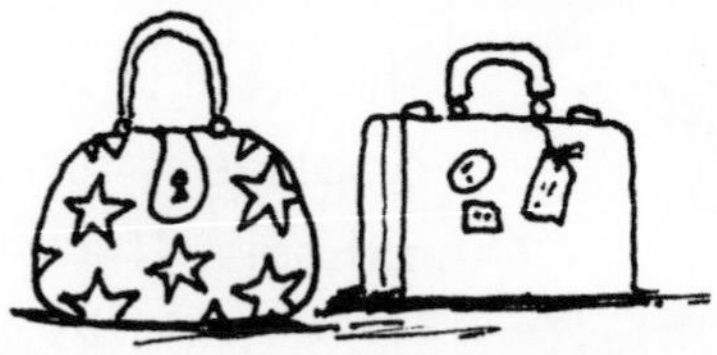

_______________ suitcases and other bags

_______________ a place where things from the past are displayed

_______________ a place to eat

_______________ take a trip to another place

_______________ includes hotels, motels and caravans

_______________ what tourists do

Tip!

A **mnemonic** is a memory trick. Anything that can help you remember something more easily is a mnemonic.
Caravan starts with car and is followed by a van.

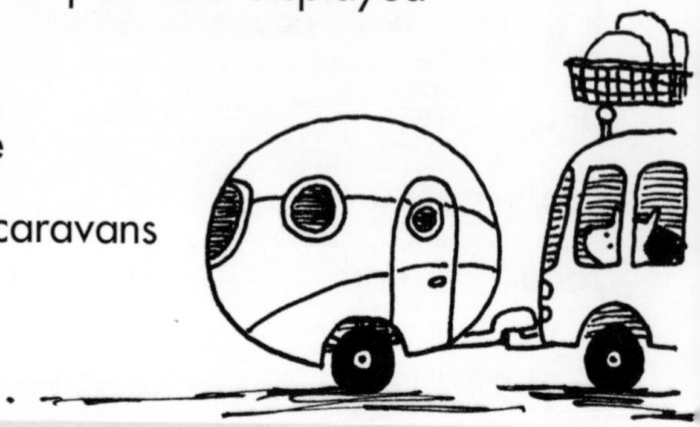

5 Write or draw your own mnemonic for these words.

restaurant	**accommodation**

6 The country or city in which each attraction is found is hidden in each sentence. Circle the letters and write the city/country in the box.

[ ] Mr Chuparis afraid of heights and will not be climbing the Eiffel Tower.

[ ] Joanne Palmer is looking forward to walking on the lower slopes of Mount Everest.

[ ] I could not understand our guide at the Taj Mahal as he spoke in dialect.

[ ] Sue wrote a poem about the Leaning Tower of Pisa. Her dad thought it a lyrical miracle.

Unit 35 Revision

The weather on the planet Neptune is seriously extreme. The wind can blow at up to 2000 km/h!

1 Write double consonants to complete these words.

te _ _ ific   su _ _ est   a _ _ raction   ha _ _ ine _ _

pre _ _ ure   so _ _ ow   exce _ _ ent   emba _ _ a _ _

reco _ _ end   a _ _ ow   a _ _ istant   sa _ _ hire

2 Form antonyms by adding a prefix from the box to each word. Use a different prefix each time.

> mis   in   il   un   dis

_____advantage   _____complete   _____pleasant   _____behave   _____logical

3 Write an antonym for each word. (Clue: Each antonym has five letters.)

late _____   exit _____   dead _____

last _____   end _____   tight _____

light _____   approximate _____   small _____

4 Write a synonym for each word. (Clue: Each synonym has an **er** sound, although the spelling may be different.)

happen _____   diary _____   travel _____

practice _____   sure _____   manners _____

5 Complete the tables.

verb	noun
	survival
grow	
	pleasure
interrupt	
	breath

noun	adjective
	logical
guilt	
	courageous
	energetic

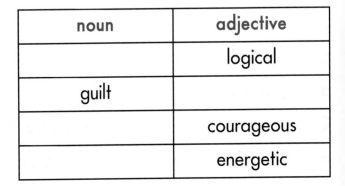

6 ✏️ Write a more interesting word for the underlined word or words.

Kerry <u>looked</u> everywhere for the earring she lost. _____

I was <u>happy</u> that we won the match. _____

John was surprised when a fox suddenly <u>came out</u>. _____

Sam was <u>very tired</u> after the school tour. _____

7 👁️ These words are sometimes confused. Colour the correct word.

The dog escaped because the | not | knot | had come | lose | loose |.

I | wander | wonder | | were | where | I can hide Mum's present.

| Weather | Whether | it rains or not, I | expect | except | we will enjoy our class picnic.

8 ✏️ You are spending your holidays in Antarctica. Write a postcard to your friend.

To _____

_____

_____

_____

_____

9 👁️ There are too many double letters in this passage. Circle the words that are wrong and write them correctly.

Michelle loves working at the computer. She ussually

spends an hour each night emailling cartoons and

photos to her friends. This year she has designed

a speciall card to give to each of her teachers for

Christmass. On the front of each card is a picture

of the teacher wearing a silly Santa hat!

_____

_____

_____

_____

_____

Unit 1
realise
suppose
choose
revise
complete
arrange
escape
collide
assume
conclude
declare
disease

Unit 2
begin
forget
regret
occur
prefer
enter
offer
answer
visit
happen
target
detail

Unit 3
waste
blame
behave
describe
recognise
remove
include
hurry
deny
reply
require
simplify

Unit 4
calf
golf
gulf
stiff

sniff
bluff
gruff
proof
wharf
dwarf
engulf
behalf

Unit 5
laugh
toughen
graph
photograph
telegraph
telephone
sphere
trophy
alphabet
phrase
phantom
physical

Unit 7
deaf
dead
ahead
heavy
health
meant
instead
least
eager
speak
pleasant
weather

Unit 8
direction
suggestion
location
separation
confusion
decision
conclusion
greatness
selfishness

stubbornness
cleanliness
forgetfulness

Unit 9
stage
bandage
large
charge
sponge
bulge
fringe
merge
surge
danger
stranger
siege

Unit 10
edge
hedge
badge
ridge
fridge
bridge
judge
trudge
smudge
dodge
fidget
gadget

Unit 11
lose
loose
breath
breathe
desert
dessert
principal
principle
wonder
wander
waist
whether

Unit 13
frown
prowl
owner
towel
allow
pillow
narrow
sorrow
powder
tomorrow
coward
knowledge

Unit 14
certain
permanent
turtle
return
curtain
further
search
research
earth
early
rehearsal
courtesy

Unit 15
sure
assure
pressure
ashamed
cushion
fashion
passion
special
ancient
machine
parachute
patient

Unit 16
pure
nature
future
failure

creature
feature
measure
pleasure
leisure
adventure
furniture
temperature

Unit 17
ruby
scarlet
lilac
violet
emerald
indigo
crimson
azure
khaki
ochre
turquoise
sapphire

Unit 19
fourth
fifth
eighth
ninth
twelfth
growth
warmth
length
strength
width
depth
breadth

Unit 20
basic
panic
picnic
magic
mimic
logic
fantastic
terrific
gigantic

energetic
automatic
enthusiastic

Unit 21
final
logical
magical
capital
national
natural
hospital
digital
criminal
critical
survival
emotional

Unit 22
eleven
twelve
thirteen
fourteen
fifteen
twenty
thirty
forty
fifty
hundred
thousand
million

Unit 23
accept
appear
effect
accuse
approach
announce
possess
embarrass
necessary
recommend
occasion
aggressive

Unit 25
germ
ginger
gently
general
average
generous
religion
intelligent
generation
advantage
emergency
gymnasium

Unit 26
since
circle
centre
cinema
recent
sincere
science
scent
scenery
scissors
delicious
conscious

Unit 27
famous
nervous
dangerous
jealous
courageous
serious
furious
cautious
envious
precious
spacious
various

Unit 28
furry
woolly
weary
guilty

shiny
icy
sorry
fantasy
variety
mystery
system
pyramid

Unit 29
computer
laptop
email
Internet
mobile
keyboard
programme
icon
download
insert
delete
barcode

Unit 31
niece
belief
relieve
achieve
receive
receipt
deceive
ceiling
foreign
weird
reign
seize

Unit 32
exact
example
exaggerate
explain
expensive
exercise
excite
excellent
except

exhausted
extinction
extremely

Unit 33
author
grocer
carpenter
lawyer
assistant
accountant
electrician
politician
journalist
pharmacist
chef
pilot

Unit 34
travel
relax
journey
caravan
luggage
budget
museum
attraction
entertainment
accommodation
sightseeing
restaurant

LIST WORDS IN ALPHABETICAL ORDER

Word	Unit	Word	Unit	Word	Unit	Word	Unit
accept	Unit 23	carpenter	Unit 33	download	Unit 29	foreign	Unit 31
accommodation	Unit 34	cautious	Unit 27	dwarf	Unit 4	forget	Unit 2
accountant	Unit 33	ceiling	Unit 31			forgetfulness	Unit 8
accuse	Unit 23	centre	Unit 26	eager	Unit 7	forty	Unit 22
achieve	Unit 31	certain	Unit 14	early	Unit 14	fourteen	Unit 22
advantage	Unit 25	charge	Unit 9	earth	Unit 14	fourth	Unit 19
adventure	Unit 16	chef	Unit 33	edge	Unit 10	fridge	Unit 10
aggressive	Unit 23	choose	Unit 1	effect	Unit 23	fringe	Unit 9
ahead	Unit 7	cinema	Unit 26	eighth	Unit 19	frown	Unit 13
allow	Unit 13	circle	Unit 26	electrician	Unit 33	furious	Unit 27
alphabet	Unit 5	cleanliness	Unit 8	eleven	Unit 22	furniture	Unit 16
ancient	Unit 15	collide	Unit 1	email	Unit 29	furry	Unit 28
announce	Unit 23	complete	Unit 1	embarrass	Unit 23	further	Unit 14
answer	Unit 2	computer	Unit 29	emerald	Unit 17	future	Unit 16
appear	Unit 23	conclude	Unit 1	emergency	Unit 25		
approach	Unit 23	conclusion	Unit 8	emotional	Unit 21	gadget	Unit 10
arrange	Unit 1	confusion	Unit 8	energetic	Unit 20	general	Unit 25
ashamed	Unit 15	conscious	Unit 26	engulf	Unit 4	generation	Unit 25
assistant	Unit 33	courageous	Unit 27	enter	Unit 2	generous	Unit 25
assume	Unit 1	courtesy	Unit 14	entertainment	Unit 34	gently	Unit 25
assure	Unit 15	coward	Unit 13	enthusiastic	Unit 20	germ	Unit 25
attraction	Unit 34	creature	Unit 16	envious	Unit 27	gigantic	Unit 20
author	Unit 33	criminal	Unit 21	escape	Unit 1	ginger	Unit 25
automatic	Unit 20	crimson	Unit 17	exact	Unit 32	golf	Unit 4
average	Unit 25	critical	Unit 21	exaggerate	Unit 32	graph	Unit 5
azure	Unit 17	curtain	Unit 14	example	Unit 32	greatness	Unit 8
		cushion	Unit 15	excellent	Unit 32	grocer	Unit 33
badge	Unit 10			except	Unit 32	growth	Unit 19
bandage	Unit 9	danger	Unit 9	excite	Unit 32	gruff	Unit 4
barcode	Unit 29	dangerous	Unit 27	exercise	Unit 32	guilty	Unit 28
basic	Unit 20	dead	Unit 7	exhausted	Unit 32	gulf	Unit 4
begin	Unit 2	deaf	Unit 7	expensive	Unit 32	gymnasium	Unit 25
behalf	Unit 4	deceive	Unit 31	explain	Unit 32		
behave	Unit 3	decision	Unit 8	extinction	Unit 32	happen	Unit 2
belief	Unit 31	declare	Unit 1	extremely	Unit 32	health	Unit 7
blame	Unit 3	delete	Unit 29			heavy	Unit 7
bluff	Unit 4	delicious	Unit 26	failure	Unit 16	hedge	Unit 10
breadth	Unit 19	deny	Unit 3	famous	Unit 27	hospital	Unit 21
breath	Unit 11	depth	Unit 19	fantastic	Unit 20	hundred	Unit 22
breathe	Unit 11	describe	Unit 3	fantasy	Unit 28	hurry	Unit 3
bridge	Unit 10	desert	Unit 11	fashion	Unit 15		
budget	Unit 34	dessert	Unit 11	feature	Unit 16	icon	Unit 29
bulge	Unit 9	detail	Unit 2	fidget	Unit 10	icy	Unit 28
		digital	Unit 21	fifteen	Unit 22	include	Unit 3
calf	Unit 4	direction	Unit 8	fifth	Unit 19	indigo	Unit 17
capital	Unit 21	disease	Unit 1	fifty	Unit 22	insert	Unit 29
caravan	Unit 34	dodge	Unit 10	final	Unit 21	instead	Unit 7

intelligent	Unit 25	occasion	Unit 23	remove	Unit 3
Internet	Unit 29	occur	Unit 2	reply	Unit 3
		ochre	Unit 17	require	Unit 3
jealous	Unit 27	offer	Unit 2	research	Unit 14
journalist	Unit 33	owner	Unit 13	restaurant	Unit 34
journey	Unit 34			return	Unit 14
judge	Unit 10	panic	Unit 20	revise	Unit 1
		parachute	Unit 15	ridge	Unit 10
keyboard	Unit 29	passion	Unit 15	ruby	Unit 17
khaki	Unit 17	patient	Unit 15		
knowledge	Unit 13	permanent	Unit 14	sapphire	Unit 17
		phantom	Unit 5	scarlet	Unit 17
laptop	Unit 29	pharmacist	Unit 33	scenery	Unit 26
large	Unit 9	photograph	Unit 5	scent	Unit 26
laugh	Unit 5	phrase	Unit 5	science	Unit 26
lawyer	Unit 33	physical	Unit 5	scissors	Unit 26
least	Unit 7	picnic	Unit 20	search	Unit 14
leisure	Unit 16	pillow	Unit 13	seize	Unit 31
length	Unit 19	pilot	Unit 33	selfishness	Unit 8
lilac	Unit 17	pleasant	Unit 7	separation	Unit 8
location	Unit 8	pleasure	Unit 16	serious	Unit 27
logic	Unit 20	politician	Unit 33	shiny	Unit 28
logical	Unit 21	possess	Unit 23	siege	Unit 9
loose	Unit 11	powder	Unit 13	sightseeing	Unit 34
lose	Unit 11	precious	Unit 27	simplify	Unit 3
luggage	Unit 34	prefer	Unit 2	since	Unit 26
		pressure	Unit 15	sincere	Unit 26
machine	Unit 15	principal	Unit 11	smudge	Unit 10
magic	Unit 20	principle	Unit 11	sniff	Unit 4
magical	Unit 21	programme	Unit 29	sorrow	Unit 13
meant	Unit 7	proof	Unit 4	sorry	Unit 28
measure	Unit 16	prowl	Unit 13	spacious	Unit 27
merge	Unit 9	pure	Unit 16	speak	Unit 7
million	Unit 22	pyramid	Unit 28	special	Unit 15
mimic	Unit 20			sphere	Unit 5
mobile	Unit 29	realise	Unit 1	sponge	Unit 9
museum	Unit 34	receipt	Unit 31	stage	Unit 9
mystery	Unit 28	receive	Unit 31	stiff	Unit 4
		recent	Unit 26	stranger	Unit 9
narrow	Unit 13	recognise	Unit 3	strength	Unit 19
national	Unit 21	recommend	Unit 23	stubbornness	Unit 8
natural	Unit 21	regret	Unit 2	suggestion	Unit 8
nature	Unit 16	rehearsal	Unit 14	suppose	Unit 1
necessary	Unit 23	reign	Unit 31	sure	Unit 15
nervous	Unit 27	relax	Unit 34	surge	Unit 9
niece	Unit 31	relieve	Unit 31	survival	Unit 21
ninth	Unit 19	religion	Unit 25	system	Unit 28

SPELLING RULES AND TIPS

Adding es, ed and ing

If a word ends in silent e, drop the e before adding the suffixes ed or ing.

smile → *smiled*   *ride* → *riding*

If a word ends in y, change y to i before adding es or ed.

try → *tries*   *spy* → *spied*

But keep the y when adding ing.

try → *trying*

If a verb ends in ic, when you add ed or ing add a k to keep the hard c sound.

mimic → *mimicked, mimicking*

But the verb stays the same when s is added.

mimic → *mimics*

Adding y

If a word has a single vowel followed by a single consonant, double the consonant before adding y.

mud → *muddy*

If a word ends in silent e, drop the e before adding y.

juice → *juicy*

Adding ous

If the base word ends in silent e, drop the e before adding ous.

fame → *famous*

If the base word ends in ce, change the e to i before adding ous.

space → *spacious*

If the base word ends in ge, keep the e when adding ous.

courage → *courageous*

If the base word ends in y, change y to i before adding ous.

envy → *envious*

Adding ion

Some verbs can be changed into nouns by adding ion.

act → *action*

If the verb ends in silent e, drop the e before adding ion.

create → *creation*

If the verb ends in de, change de to s before adding ion.

divide → *division*